Copyright Notice 2023:

CW00542782

MUSHROOM

COLORING BOOK ADULTS

Thank you!

Dear Reader,
We poured our hearts into creating this book for you. As a small family company, we are filled with gratitude for your support. To show our appreciation, we have a special surprise for you- a free BONUS that we hope will serve as a cherished keepsake. Please scan the QR code above to claim your surprise.

This book belongs to

- -

- -

Milton Keynes UK
Ingram Content Group UK Ltd.
UKHW051951301123
433416UK00026B/759